Ready to Read
Fairy Tales

How to Pla

1. Press the Power button to turn the SD-X R~~e~~~~a~~~~der~~ on or off. The LED will light up when the SD-X Reader is on.

2. Touch the volume buttons found on this page to adjust the volume.

3. Touch words and pictures on the page to hear audio. These icons start the following activities:

   - Hear the Page
   - Hear the Word
   - Spell the Word
   - Sound Out the Word
   - Find It
   - Word Play
   - Hear the Music
   - Sing Along

4. Find the monkey on each spread and touch him with the SD-X Reader.

5. After two minutes of inactivity, the SD-X Reader will beep and go to sleep.

6. If the batteries are low, the SD-X Reader will beep twice and the LED will start blinking. Replace the batteries by following the instructions on the preceding page. The SD-X Reader uses two AAA batteries.

7. To use headphones or earbuds, plug them into the headphone jack on the SD-X Reader.

Volume

 Publications International, Ltd.

The Ugly Duckling

Once upon a time, six baby ducks pop out of their shells.

One duck looks different.

Mother Duck says: You are not yellow. You are gray. But I love you. You are my baby duck.

The baby ducks swim
with Mother Duck. They
meet other birds.

A rooster says to the gray
duck: You are different. You
are an ugly duckling.

The duckling is sad.

He swims away from
his family.

The duckling sees a family of geese.

The geese ask: Are you lost?

The duckling says: No. I do not live with my family. I am too ugly.

The geese say: Come with us.

The duckling says: O.K.

A dog runs to the geese. He barks.

The geese are scared. They fly away.

The duckling frowns.

He says: I am alone again.

A woman finds the duckling. She
takes him home.

The woman says: You may live here.

A cat and a chicken live with
the woman.

The cat says: You look strange.

The chicken says: You are ugly.

The duckling is sad. He leaves
the home.

The duckling walks in the snow. He is cold.

He finds a tree. He makes a bed.

The duckling waits for spring.

He says: I miss my family.

The duckling says: Spring is here.

He still misses his family.

He sees four swans.

The duckling says: You are pretty swans.

The swans say: Not as pretty as you.

The duckling looks at himself in the water.
He is now a pretty swan.

He says: I am not ugly.

He tells the swans his story.

They say: We will help you find your family.

They go to the pond where his family lives.

They find his brothers, sisters, and Mother Duck.

His brothers and sisters say: You are pretty.

Mother Duck says: I love you now, Pretty Swan. I loved you then, Gray Duck. This pond is your home.

Goldilocks and the Three Bears

Once upon a time, there were three bears: Papa Bear, Mama Bear, and Baby Bear.

Today, Mama Bear makes three bowls of cereal. The big bowl is for Papa Bear. The medium bowl is for Mama Bear. The little bowl is for Baby Bear.

The cereal is too hot to eat. The three bears must wait. They walk in the forest.

A girl goes to the bears' house. Her name is Goldilocks.

She sees the bowls of cereal. She is hungry.

Goldilocks tries the big bowl.

She says: Too hot.

Goldilocks tries the medium bowl.

She says: Too cold.

Goldilocks tries the little bowl.

She says: Just right.

She eats all the cereal in the bowl.

Goldilocks sees three chairs.

The big chair is for Papa Bear. The medium chair is for Mama Bear. The little chair is for Baby Bear.

Goldilocks sits in the big chair.

She says: Too hard.

Goldilocks sits in the medium chair.

She says: Too soft.

Goldilocks sits in the little chair.

She says: Just right.

Goldilocks leans back. The chair breaks.

Goldilocks goes to the bedroom.
She sees three beds.

The big bed is for Papa Bear. The
medium bed is for Mama Bear.
The little bed is for Baby Bear.

Goldilocks rests in the
big bed.

She says: Too hard.

Goldilocks rests in the
medium bed.

She says: Too soft.

Goldilocks rests in
the little bed.

She says: Just right.

She falls asleep.

The three bears come home. They want to eat their cereal.

Papa Bear looks at his bowl. His spoon is dirty.

Mama Bear looks at her bowl. Her spoon is dirty.

Baby Bear looks at his bowl. His cereal is gone!

Baby Bear cries.

The three bears go to the living room.
They see the broken chair.

Baby Bear says: My chair is broken!

Papa Bear says: Someone is here.

Mama Bear says: We will look in
the bedroom.

Papa Bear looks at his bed.

He says: My bed is a mess.

Mama Bear looks at her bed.

She says: My bed is a mess.

Baby Bear looks at his bed.

He says: Someone is in my bed!

Goldilocks wakes up.

Papa Bear asks: Who are you?

Goldilocks does not wait. She goes to the window. She jumps to the ground. Then she runs home.

The three bears never see Goldilocks again. They will always wonder who she is.

The Frog Prince

Once upon a time, a princess plays with a gold ball.

The princess throws the ball into a pond. She wants to see what will happen.

The ball sinks to the bottom.

She cries: My ball is gone.

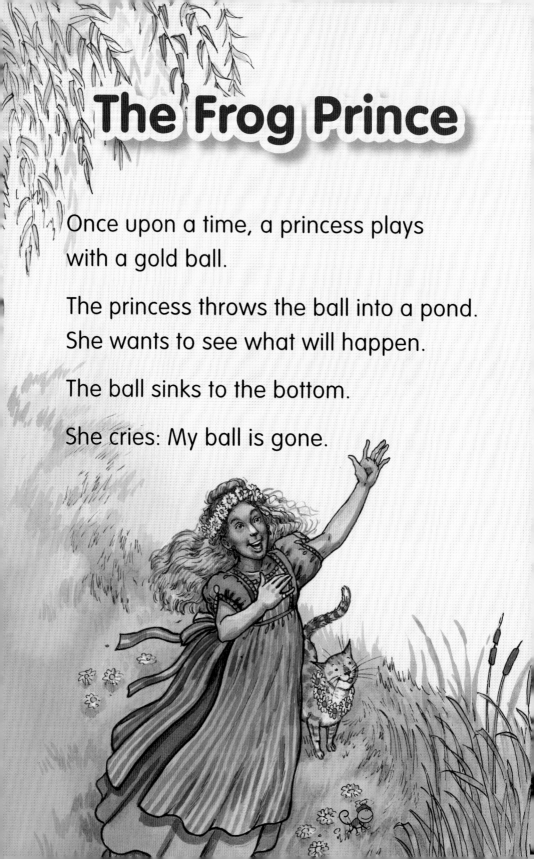

The princess sees a frog by the shore.

The frog says: I will find your ball. But you must be my friend.

The princess does not like frogs. They are green and ugly.

The princess pretends to like the frog. She says: I will be your friend.

The frog finds the ball. He gives it to the princess. Then the princess runs away.

The frog yells: Wait for me!

The frog follows the princess home.

He sits on her table. He eats her food. He makes a mess.

The princess gets mad.

She says: Stop! Do not make a mess.

The princess hits the table with her hand. The frog falls off the table.

The princess looks at the ground. The frog is now a prince.

The princess says: Who are you?

He says: A prince. You have saved me.

The princess says: How?

The prince says: A witch turned me into a frog. There is just one way to break the spell.

The princess asks: What is it?

The prince says: A princess must get mad at me.

The prince and the princess fall in love.

The prince asks the princess: Will you marry me?

The princess says: Yes!

Many people go to the wedding. They clap. They cheer.

The prince and the princess go to their new home. They are happy.

The prince asks: Do you like frogs now?

The princess laughs.

She says: Yes. I like frogs.

Twinkle, Twinkle, Little Star

Twinkle, twinkle, little star,

How I wonder what you are.

Up above the world so high,

Like a diamond in the sky.

Twinkle, twinkle, little star,

How I wonder what you are.